Spell It!

Book 1

Patricia Lewis

Illustrated by Tod Lewis

CONTENTS

Preface

Spell it! is a spelling scheme in four stages for pupils of 7 to 11 years. It is designed for teachers to use in the classroom with small groups or on a one-to-one basis.

The scheme is multi-sensory: it teaches by using all the pupil's sensory channels – the visual, the auditory, the tactile and the kinaesthetic (ie the muscular effort of the body). It is structured and cumulative, in that each section of learning leads to the next and each section builds on what has been taught previously. However, it is also possible for most of the sections to be used independently.

The scheme includes the 300 key words which constitute 50–75 percent of those used in English (see McNally and Murray, 1984). Beyond these, words have been selected according to the frequency of their use from the *Thorndike Illustrated Junior Dictionary*.

The scheme presupposes knowledge of letters and their sounds, and of consonant blends. The notes for each section indicate where the teacher should check for knowledge of consonant blends. Pupils who still experience difficulty with any of these should receive additional help.

How to use the pupils' pages
The title of each section incorporates the spelling pattern to be taught, for instance

Don't duck 'ck'

followed by a picture. The teacher should discuss the picture briefly with the pupils:

What is happening in the picture?
Is there more than one meaning, then, for the word 'duck'? Can you think of others?

The pupil then reads aloud each word in the list. Pupil or teacher then reads aloud the questions which follow and the pupil answers them. At this stage, the teacher can introduce the teaching point given in the notes (see pages 5–8).

The teacher dictates each of the words in the list and the pupil writes them in pencil on a separate sheet. This cuts out the visual channel (the strongest channel, which tends to mask the others) and provides auditory input. The individual letters of each word should be dictated; at the same time consonant blends and letter strings should be pointed out and emphasised, for example: "The first word is spoon – 'sp', that is, 's', 'p'; 'oo', which is 'o', 'o', and then 'n'." The words should be checked and any incorrectly-spelled words dictated again.

A separate *key word* appears on each page, away from the main list. Most of these key words are irregular words which do not fit into any word family, either phonically or visually. They therefore require a

different kind of teaching. It is recommended that these are taught by a modified form of the Fernald Tracing Technique (see Thomson, 1984):

1 The teacher writes the word in large print, using wax crayon, on a piece of card about 6 cm x 30 cm.
2 The pupil traces the letters with a finger, saying each part quietly.
3 This is repeated until the pupil can write the word from memory. The word must always be written as a whole unit from the beginning. In the case of interruption or error, it must be started again.
4 When the word has been written in rough, the pupil can write it in a story, under a picture etc – saying it quietly as he or she writes it.
5 The teacher types out what the pupil writes, and he or she reads it back the next day.

The pupil now works through the remaining activities on the sheet. Some activities involve writing from memory fun sentences which incorporate three or four of the words in the list. Word association and imagery have long been recognised as one of the most effective ways of absorbing information, since the visual/pictorial memory is stronger than the visual/verbal memory. For this reason, the sentences are accompanied by illustrations.

Other activities include crosswords, wordsearches, pictures, word puzzles, mazes, 'whodunnits' (in which the pupil is required to be a detective) and adventure activities. The last of these require the pupil to find the way out of a 'danger' situation (a haunted house or a desert, for example) and include practice in following instructions, sequencing and orientation by way of up/down, left/right, N/S/E/W and so on.

Each of these activities incorporates five or six more of the words in the list. Any remaining words in the list are usually incorporated in a further short activity, riddle or joke. Most pupils prefer to solve the puzzles without referring to the word list. However, it is important that pupils understand that answers to most of the puzzles are contained in the list, so that they are never at a loss over what to write.

The importance of writing the words from memory cannot be overemphasised, for this is how pupils learn to spell. Where an activity requires the pupil to write more than three words at a time from memory, the initial letter of each word is provided. The pupil should cover up the words and use these initial letters as reminders. Of course, some pupils will not be able to remember the words, even when reminders are provided. For these pupils, the teacher will need to dictate the words. Each word that is spelled wrongly should be written again from memory – more than once, if necessary – until the pupil can write it correctly.

A week after the section has been worked through, the teacher should dictate the relevant sentence to test pupils' retention of the words learned. The teacher dictates the sentence and the pupil repeats it. The teacher dictates it again and the pupil writes it, saying each word, and then reads aloud what he or she has written. The pupil should be encouraged to discover any errors, the teacher prompting with clues, if necessary, eg

Look carefully at your first sentence.

or, if this is not enough:

Remember that we drop the 'e' when we add a vowel suffix.

Spelling errors should be noted and further practice given. Nowhere in the scheme is a pupil required to write a spelling pattern which has not already been taught.

When the pupil has finished working through a section the teacher should ask him or her to write a few sentences of his or her own, using words chosen from those learned. In this way, the pupil is likely to home in on words which are of most importance to him or her. Further reinforcement is thus provided for the words the pupil is likely to use most.

At the end of each section in the Notes a further list of words in the same word family is provided together with a revision exercise for the pupil. This gives an opportunity for more practice.

It will be noted that the short vowels are taught in alphabetical order, the purpose being to reinforce knowledge of the vowels in the order in which they usually appear. However, some pupils may have difficulty in discriminating between the short sounds of 'e' and 'i' and the teacher may prefer to teach the short vowels in the order of 'a' 'i' 'o' 'e' 'u'. The cumulation of words taught in the short vowel section is unaffected by change of order and the dictation sentences may still be given with the knowledge that the child is asked to write only those words he has been taught.

It is recommended that the teacher encourages pupils to attempt to use the words learned in a section in written stories and other schoolwork during the week, so that further reinforcement is provided.

A file could be built up for each pupil, containing the sections worked, with a personal index so that the pupil can easily refer to any section.

Diacritical marks

Letters are indicated with ' ': 'a'.
Sounds of letters are indicated as //: /ar/.
Short vowel sounds are marked with ˘: /ă/.
Long vowel sounds are marked with ¯: /ā/.

References
McNally, J. and Murray, W. (1984) *Key Words to Literacy and the Teaching of Reading* The Teacher Publishing Company Ltd, Kettering, Northants.
Thomson, M. (1984) *Developmental Dyslexia* Edward Arnold, London.
Thorndike, E.L. (1942) *Thorndike Junior Illustrated Dictionary* University of London Press, Ltd.

Teaching points

The following is a list of the teaching points in the order in which they are given over the four stages, together with test words for each point. The teacher is advised to use the test words diagnostically and to ascertain the point in the scheme at which the pupil is to enter. Each word should first be dictated on its own, then in a sentence – for example: '*meat*: I like meat for dinner.') In this way, the pupil is left in no doubt as to the meaning of the word.

Teaching point		*Test words*		
BOOK 1	short 'a'	can	fat	has
	short 'e'	bed	ten	men
	short 'i'	pig	in	sit
	short 'o'	dog	hot	box
	short 'u'	but	run	must
	'ar' digraph	farm	smart	car
	'or' digraph	fork	storm	sport
	'sh' digraph	shop	shut	fish
	'ch' digraph	chip	torch	lunch
	'th' digraph	thin	that	with
	'ck'	back	pick	sock
	'll'	tell	doll	full
	'all'	ball	call	small
	'ss' endings	miss	cross	dress
	'ff' endings	stuff	off	cliff
	'wa'	wasp	want	wash
	'war'	warm	worn	ward
	'wor'	worm	work	worse
	'a' before 'l'	talk	walk	salt
	'er' digraph	better	sister	dinner
	'y' at the end of a word	happy	empty	twenty
	'a' sounding as /ar/	father	after	grass
	'ed' endings	packed	jumped	wished
	a–e	game	grape	plate
	'are' sounding as /aer/	stare	scare	dare
	i–e	smile	fine	time
	o–e	bone	rope	nose
	u–e	use	sure	rude
BOOK 2	'o' sounding as /ŭ/	mother	love	oven
	'tch'	fetch	match	switch
	soft 'c'	face	nice	except
	words beginning with 'k'	king	kite	kick
	soft 'g'	stage	large	change
	words beginning with 'j'	jelly	joke	jug
	'dge' endings	bridge	badge	hedge
	'age' endings	message	village	cottage
	'u' as a wall after 'g'	guess	guide	tongue
	long vowel sounds with short vowel spellings	find	most	cold
	'ea' sounding as /ē/	meat	beach	please
	'ai'	nail	train	chair
	'igh'	might	fright	light
	'oa'	boat	loaf	coal
	'oo' sounding as /oo/	food	spoon	mood
	'oo' sounding as /u/	book	wool	cook
	'y' and 'ie' as word endings sounding as /ī/	fly	die	sky
	'ay'	away	play	tray
	'ew'	few	threw	stew
	'ee'	teeth	leeks	coffee
	'ui' sounding as /oo/ and /ī/	fruit	build	cruise
	'ow' sounding as /ō/	yellow	grow	blow
	'ea' sounding as /ĕ/	head	breath	threat
	'oi'	boil	coin	oil
BOOK 3	'ou' sounding as /ow/	round	house	count
	'au'	haunt	fault	laundry
	'ue' endings	true	Tuesday	glue
	'oy'	enjoy	boy	royal
	'ow' sounding as /ow/	town	tower	crown
	'ou' sounding as /oo/ and /ū/	soup	cousin	country
	'aw'	lawn	paws	awful
	Suffixing: doubling the consonant	sitting	winner	stopped
	just adding on – 1 (No doubling)	spilling	feeling	doing
	dropping the 'e'	making	hoped	famous
	just adding on – 2 (No dropping)	nicely	useful	careless
	changing 'y' to 'i' – 1			
	changing 'y' to 'i' – 2	babies	pies	uglier
	keeping the 'y'	enjoyed	studying	worrying
	'tion' endings	station	mention	information
	'le' endings (1)	table	eagle	idle
	'le' endings (2)	battle	saddle	giggle

Teaching point		Test words		
BOOK 3 (cont.)	'able' endings	enjoyable	valuable	comfortable
	'ic' endings	picnic	music	elastic
	'ur'	church	purse	murder
	'ible' endings	possible	terrible	sensible
	'ckle' endings	buckle	crackle	prickle
	'el' endings	travel	label	chapel
	doubling on multi-syllable words	travelling	forgotten	marvellous
	'ear' sounding as /er/	learn	heard	earn
BOOK 4	'ch' sounding as /k/ and /sh/	chemist	ache	machine
	'ph' sounding as /f/	photograph	elephant	orphan
	'al' endings	hospital	animal	unusual
	'ir'	circus	shirt	bird
	'ough'	through	cough	tough
	'ought'	bought	ought	brought
	'ie'	thief	fierce	shield
	'ci'	precious	special	anxious
	'our' endings	colour	tour	favour
	'ory' endings	factory	story	memory
	'ei' sounding as /ā/	weigh	seize	receipt
	'ssion' endings	confession	permission	discussion
	'ie' as /yĕ/	diet	obedient	alien
	'ture' endings	picture	future	furniture
	'ar' endings	burglar	collar	popular
	'aught'	naughty	taught	caught
	'sion' endings	television	division	collision
	'ery' endings	slippery	surgery	nursery
	'ia' as /yă/	brilliant	dial	diary
	'or' endings	actor	doctor	professor
	silent 'w'	write	wrap	wrong
	'io' as /yŭ/	million	onion	furious
	'ary' endings	necessary	library	dictionary

Notes

1 Short 'a'

Teaching points/checks
- The letter 'a' has the sound /ă/ as in *can*.
- Capital D for Dad.
- At this stage, the sound /k/ at the beginning of a word is spelt with 'c' as in *can*.

Dictation
1 Dad has a hat.
2 The fat man had a can.

More words for practice
bad bat ham jam mat pat pan ran rat sat Sam tan

2 Short 'e'

Teaching points/checks
- The letter 'e' has the sound /ĕ/ as in *get*.
- Check knowledge of consonant blends 'sl' and 'pt' as in *slept*.

Dictation
1 Yes, Dad has a bed.
2 The ten men slept.
3 Let Dad get the red van.

More words for practice
fed led hen net pet set wet beg peg bet met

3 Short 'i'

Teaching points/checks

- The letter 'i' has the sound /ĭ/ as in *bit*.
- Check knowledge of consonant blend 'nd' as in *and*.

Dictation
1 Dad has a pig and it bit him.
2 Dad can sit in the bin.
3 The van is big.

More words for practice
hid lid pin tin fit hit lit wig win

4 Short 'o'

Teaching points/checks
- The letter 'o' has the sound /ŏ/ as in *box*.
- Check knowledge of consonant blends 'st' in *stop* and *lost* and 'fr' as in *from*.

Dictation
1 Stop the van.
2 He lost the hat he got from Dad.
3 Dad has a box of hot dogs.

More words for practice
fog hop log lot mop cot pot fox nod rod

5 Short 'u'

Teaching points/checks
- The letter 'u' has the sound /ŭ/ as in *run*.
- 'a' 'e' 'i' 'o' 'u' are all vowels. All the sounds taught have been *short* vowel sounds. All other letters of the alphabet are called *consonants*. Teach this word if the pupil can manage it. Otherwise introduce it later.

Dictation

1 Dad must run and get the bus.
2 The sun is just up.
3 Mum has a cut.

More words for practice

bun brush gun cup mug hut sum nut crush
hug plum rush thrush chug

Revision: Short 'a' 'e' 'i' 'o' 'u'
Dictation

1 Dad is in the bus.
2 Get the box for Mum.
3 Mum has the big bed.

6 'ar'
Teaching points/checks

- 'a' and 'r' together make the sound /ar/.
- At this stage the sound /k/ at the end of a word is spelt with 'k', as in *dark*. So the sound /k/ is spelt with 'c' at the beginning of a word and with 'k' at the end.
- Check knowledge of consonant blend 'sm' as in *smart*.

Dictation

1 The car is smart but it has a mark on it.
2 I hit my arm in the dark.
3 Mum and Dad are at the farm.

More words for practice

bar harm part dart tar barn cart tart card

7 'or'
Teaching points/checks

- The letters 'o' and 'r' together make the sound /or/.
- Check knowledge of consonant blend 'sp' as in *sport*.
- Capital 'i' for the word *I*.
- *Horse* has an 'e' on the end.

Dictation

1 Tom is a sport.
2 I must get a fork for Dad.
3 Get the horse in from the storm.

Answer

The treasure is hidden behind the stone with *storm*.

More words for practice

corn form port cord lord

8 'sh' digraph
Teaching points/checks

- 's' and 'h' together make the sound /sh/. Point out letters at the beginning and at the end of words.
- Check knowledge of consonant blend 'cr' as in *crash*.

Dictation

1 The cat is shut in the ship.
2 Tom got fish from the shop.
3 I let the dish go crash.

More words for practice

bash bush hush gush rush mash

9 'ch' digraph
Teaching points/checks

- The letters 'ch' together make a single sound.
- Check knowledge of consonant blend 'br' as in *branch*.
- Point out the 'n' sound in *pinch, punch, lunch*.
- To form the plural of many words we add 's' as in *chips*.

Dictation

1 I had chips and a chop for lunch.
2 Tom lost his torch and cut his chin.
3 Dad can chop up the branch.

More words for practice

chap chat pinch munch ranch porch

10 'th' digraph
Teaching points/checks

- The letters 'th' together make a single sound. Point out 'th' at the beginning and at the end of words.
- Point out 'n' as in *think* and *thank*.
- Check knowledge of consonant blend 'ng' as in *thing*.

Dictation

1 That man is so thin.
2 Thank Mum for the things she got.
3 I must do this and then I can go with Dad.

Revision: 'ar' 'or' 'sh' 'ch' 'th'
Dictation

1 It is dark but Tom has a torch.
2 That is the dish for the chops.

11 'ck' digraph
Teaching points/checks

- We use 'ck' after a short vowel.
- Check knowledge of consonant blend 'bl' as in *black*.

Dictation

1 Pick up the box of forks and lock it in the car.
2 Mum has dark red socks.
3 The sacks are at the back of the shop.

More words for practice

crack prick deck rock brick stack block sick
cluck shock peck struck dock thick speck stock

12 'll' endings
Teaching points/checks

- We use 'll' after a short vowel.

Dictation

1 Well, the bus is full.
2 Tell Mum that I lost my doll.
3 Will you fill my box?

More words for practice

bell fell spell yell gull bull pull dull shell
ill grill bill still frill thrill grill

13 'all' with the sound /orl/
Teaching points/checks
- 'all' makes the sound /orl/.

Dictation
1 Nick has lost all the balls.
2 I am tall but Tom is small.
3 Can we call Dad for lunch?

14 'ss' endings
Teaching points/checks
- We use 'ss' after a short vowel.
- Check knowledge of consonant blend 'pr' as in *press*.

Dictation
1 I must go and press my dress.
2 The boss is as cross as can be.
3 Miss Black is bad at chess.

More words for practice
mass lass loss moss hiss

15 'ff' endings
Teaching points/checks
- We use 'ff' after a short vowel.
- Check consonant blend 'sn' as in *sniff*.

Dictation
1 Get the stuff from the shop.
2 Let the dog sniff that fish.
3 The man fell off the cliff.

More words for practice
cuff huff puff

Revision: 'ck' 'll' 'ss' 'ff' 'all' (/orl/)
Dictation
1 The sack is full.
2 Tell the boss that Dad has all the stuff.

16 'wa'
Teaching points/checks
- 'wa' has the sound /wŏ/ as in *wasp*.
- Check knowledge of consonant blend 'sw' as in *swamp*, *swan* and *swap*.

Dictation
1 The swan will go for that wasp.
2 What do you want to do with this wand?
3 You can wash in this water.

17 'war'
Teaching points/checks
- 'war' has the sound /wor/ as in *warm*.
- Check knowledge of consonant blend 'dw' as in *dwarf*.

Dictation
1 I will warn Sam not to go to the farm.
2 Go forward and get your reward.
3 This ward is so warm.

More words for practice
award wart wharf swarthy

18 'wor'
Teaching points/checks
- 'wor' has the sound /wer/ as in *worm*.
- Take care with the 'e' on the end of *worse*.
- No English word ends in 'v'. There is always an 'e' after it as in *have*.

Dictation
1 My word! What a fat worm!
2 That cat you have is not worth all the work.
3 He is the worst man in the world.

19 'a' before 'l'
Teaching points/checks
- In some words 'a' before 'l' has the sound 'or' as in *stalk*. In some words the 'l' is sounded after the 'a' as in *salt*.
- *false* has an 'e' on the end.

Dictation
1 Give the chalk to that bald man.
2 We can walk to the shop to get salt.
3 Will you talk to me?

Revision: 'wa', 'war', 'wor', 'a' before 'l'
Dictation
1 Do you want to go for a walk?
2 I warn you it will be hard work.
3 We have to go and wash, worse luck!

20 'er'
Teaching points/checks
- 'er' is the most common spelling for this sound at the end of a word. It is unusual in the middle of a word.
- In all these words the first vowel is separated from the second by *two* consonants to keep it short. The rule that a short vowel is followed by two consonants is a very general one.

Dictation
1 Dad had better have dinner with us.
2 The butter is under that box.
3 I got a letter from my sister.

21 'y' with the sound /'ē/ at the end of a word
Teaching points/checks
- The sound /ē/ at the end of a word is spelt with a 'y'.
- Stress the 'p' in *empty*.
- Check knowledge of consonant blend 'tw' as in *twenty*.

Dictation
1 Daddy has no dogs but he has twenty pigs.
2 It was windy and Mummy lost her hat.
3 I have plenty of chips so I am happy.

More words for practice
carry lorry granny rusty cherry milky misty
fifty jolly bonny marry dotty pretty hurry
frosty

22 'a' with the sound /ar/
Teaching points/checks
- In the south of England the letter 'a' sometimes has the sound /ar/.
- 'grass' also conforms to the 'ss' ending rule.
- Check knowledge of consonant blend 'gr' as in grass.

Dictation
1 Ask my father if I can have a bath.
2 I would rather run fast than just sit on the grass.
3 Mum has a nasty cut on her leg.

More words for practice
basket daft staff glass past plaster vast

23 'ed' endings
Teaching points/checks
- We use 'ed' when we write about something that happened in the past. 'ed' never sounds like /ed/. It sounds like /t/ as in *jumped*, /d/ as in *grabbed* or /id/ as in *planted*. If the 'ed' ending is taken off it leaves the whole word. (Compare *brushed* and *slept*.) Use Ed as a character to help the children understand 'ed' endings.

Dictation
1 The dog barked but at last he slept.
2 Miss Smart sorted all the stars.
3 Tom wished he had not lost his lunch.

Revision: 'er', 'y ending', 'a' with the sound 'ar', 'ed' endings
Dictation
1 The bath was empty so Mummy filled it.
2 Tom pinched my last chip.
3 I am sorry I pushed you under the bed.

24 'a' – consonant – 'e'
Teaching points/checks
- 'e' on the end of a word is not sounded, but it makes the vowel before it long (say its name). 'a' – consonant – 'e' has the sound /ā/ as in *game*.
- Check knowledge of consonant blend 'pl' as in *plate*.

Dictation
1 The chips can go on the same plate.
2 My father gave me a grape.
3 When Tom came over we made a fishing game.

More words for practice
fade late pale rate sale stale tale cane hate mate plane scrape slate same tame

25 'are' as /aer/
Teaching points/checks
- 'are' has the sound /aer/ as in *scare*.
- Take care with the 'wh' in *when*.
- Check knowledge of consonant blends 'sc' as in *scare* and 'squ' as in *square*. 'q' is always followed by 'u'.

Dictation
1 You should not stare at that man.
2 It was fun when Dad gave us a scare.
3 Can you spare a square of that butter?

More words for practice
mare rare compare

26 'i' – consonant – 'e'
Teaching points/checks
- 'i' – consonant – 'e' has the sound /ī/ as in *smile*.
- Check knowledge of the 'wh' digraph in *white*. Emphasise the /h/ sound.

Dictation
1 If we ever have the time we must go for a ride.
2 This white dress is quite small.
3 In summer we never have games inside.

More words for practice
bite crime dive drive five hive line mine nine ripe slide stripe tide tile wise wire

27 'o' – consonant – 'e'
Teaching points/checks
- 'o' – consonant – 'e' has the sound /ō/ as in *cope*.
- The letter 'x' is *never* followed by an 's' (eg *next*).

Dictation
1 I fell over the rope and cut my nose.
2 Give the dog a bone.
3 My clothes are all at home.

More words for practice
alone cone grope pole tone dome mope vote rode

28 'u' – consonant – 'e'
Teaching points/checks
- 'u' – consonant – 'e' has the sound /ū/ as in *cure*.

Dictation
1 Can I use this box?
2 Are you sure the pills can cure you?
3 I refuse to talk to that rude man.

More words for practice
brute crude dune flute fuse prune

Revision – 'a' – consonant – 'e', 'are', 'i' – consonant – 'e', 'o' – consonant – 'e', 'u' – consonant – 'e'

Dictation
1 I made sure the tube was empty.
2 It is rude to stare.
3 It will be fine if you give Dad those plates.

1 You *can* spell these words

had	man
Dad	van
am	at
an	fat
can	has

Which letter is in every word? ....
What sound does the letter make?
Put a ring round the word at the top of the page which has the letter.

Look across the lines and find five words with the sound /ă/.
Colour each one and then write it.

```
v b h j u r t h
w o d h a d f t
b a f c a n l t
a n u p l m w q
z r e q w y u i
b g D a d f t y
c x a m j y i o
b d r t y u q a
v s d b y q i e
```

....

Now cover the five words and write them again.
Here is the first letter of each to help you: h c a D a

Key word   the

2 Look at the picture. Read the sentence aloud.
Then copy it, saying each word. Put a line under
each word with the sound /ă/.

The fat man has a van.

....

Read the sentence again until you can remember it.
Then cover it and write it again.

3 The first letter of each object spells a word with the sound /ă/.
Write the word. Then cover it and write it again.

....

2 Get going with /ĕ/

| bed | ten | yet | let | yes |
| red | men | get | leg | slept |

Which letter is in every word? ....
What sound does the letter make?
Put a ring round the word at the top of the page which has the letter.

1

Look at the picture. Read the sentence aloud. Then copy it, saying each word. Put a line under each word with /ĕ/.

Ten men slept in the bed.

....

Read the sentence aloud until you can remember it.
Then cover it and write it again.

Key word in

2

Use the picture clue to spell a word with the sound /ĕ/.
Write the word. Then cover it and write it again.

....

3

Can you drive the train through the tunnels to the station?
As you go, write the words with /ĕ/ when you meet them.

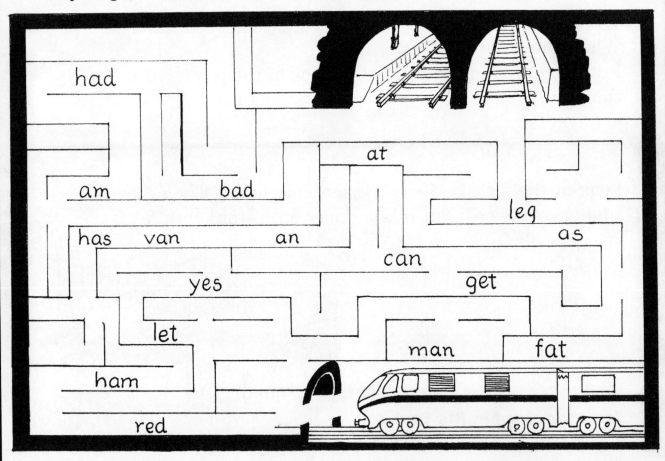

Now cover the words and write them again. Here is the first
letter of each to help you: r y g l

3 A bit of fun with /ĭ/

is	pig
it	did
if	bin
his	bit
big	sit

Which letter is in every word? ....
What sound does the letter make?
Put a ring round the word at the top of the page which has the letter.

1

What did the policeman say to his tummy?
You're under a vest.

Put a ring round the two small words with /ĭ/. Write the words. Then cover them and write them again.

Key word and

2

Look at the picture. Read the sentence aloud. Then copy it, saying each word. Put a line under each word with /ĭ/.

The pig is in the bin.

....

Read the sentence until you can remember it.
Then cover it and write it again.

3

Fill in the crossword puzzle.

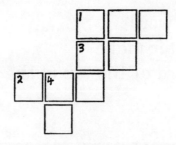

Across

1 The dog is not small. It is ——— .
2 You can ——— in a chair.
3 *sit* without the 's'.

Down

1 The dog ——— the man.
4 I will come ——— I can.

Now cover the words and write them again.
Here is the first letter of each to help you: b s i b i

4 Box clever with /ŏ/

on	dog
of	stop
not	lost
got	from
hot	box

Which letter is in every word? ....
What sound does the letter make?
Put a ring round the word at the top of the page which has the letter.

1

Look at the picture. Read the sentence aloud. Then copy it, saying each word. Put a line under each word with /ŏ/.

Tom got a hot dog in a box.

....

Read the sentence until you can remember it.
Then cover it and write it again.

Key word he

2

Shall I tell you the joke about the butter?
I'd better not. You'll only spread it.

Put a ring round the word with /ŏ/
and write it.
Then cover it and write it again.

....

3

Can you help the prince save
the princess from the burning
castle? Start at the bottom of
the ladder. Fill in the missing
letter on each step to make
words with /ŏ/.

o -

- f

sto -

- ost

- rom

Now cover the words and
write them again.
Here is the first letter of
each to help you:
f l s o o

5 Up with the flag for /ŭ/

up	but
run	bus
fun	must
sun	just
cut	Mum

Which letter is in every word? ....
What sound does the letter make?
Put a ring round the word at the top of the page which has the letter.

1

Use the picture to help you spell a word of three letters with /ŭ/.
Write the word. Then cover it and write it again.

....

Key word to

2

Look at the picture. Read the sentence aloud. Then copy it, saying each word. Put a line under each word with /ŭ/.

Mum must run to the bus.

....

Read the sentence until you can remember it.
Then cover it and write it again.

3

Who is flying which kite? Write the name of each child.
Beside it, write the words on the kite he or she is flying.

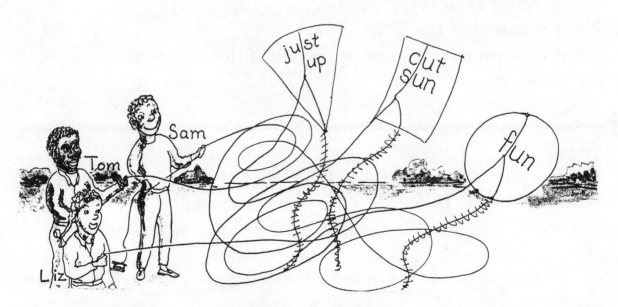

Now cover the words and write them again.
Here is the first letter of each to help you: b j u f r

Revision

A Use the clues and fill in the spaces.

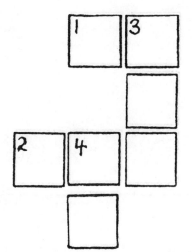

Across
1 I will come – I can.
2 Like a car. It carries goods.

Down
3 Rhymes with sun
4 'I – a boy,' said Tom.

Write the words you have written. Then cover them and write them again. Here is the first letter of each to help you:
i v f a

B Look across the lines and find the five words below.
Colour each word and write it.

| an | but | yet | did | not |

```
z  h  a  n  v  d  q  x  r  k  p
   c  b  g  b  u  t  e  p  l
      k  y  e  t  h  q  o
         a  d  i  d  n
            n  o  t
               b
```

Now cover the words and write them again. Here is the first letter of each to help you: a b y d n

6 Get a star for 'ar'

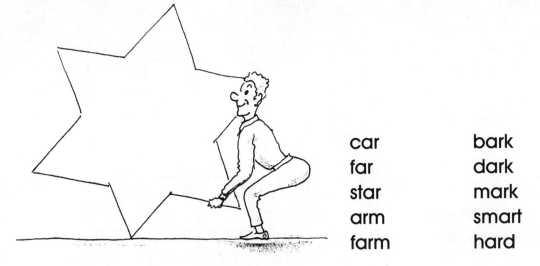

car	bark
far	dark
star	mark
arm	smart
farm	hard

Which two letters are in every word? ....
What sound do the letters make?
Put a ring round the word at the top of the page which has the letters.

1

Read across the lines, and find five words with **'ar'**.
Colour each one and write it.

```
            h
          f p n
        c v g h y
      x j m a r k p
      z d a r k j p a z
      x v h y u i o b a s t
        n c f t y h a r d
        f j f a r q p
        b a r k o
          h v r
            j
```

Now cover the words and write them again.
Here is the first letter of each to help you: m d h f b

Key word are

2 Look at the picture. Read the sentence aloud. Then copy it, saying each word. Put a line under each word with **'ar'**.

Dad has a big farm and a smart car.

....

Read the sentence until you can remember it.
Then cover it and write it again.

3 Which two objects are in the square but not in the circle? Write the word for each. Then cover the two words and write them again.

....

7 Be a sport with 'or'

or	storm
for	cork
born	fork
torn	sort
horse	sport

Which two letters are in every word? ....
What sound do the letters make?
Put a ring round the word at the top of the page which has the letters.

1

Can you find three objects with 'or' in the picture?
Write the word for each. Then cover the words
and write them again.

....

Key word   I

2

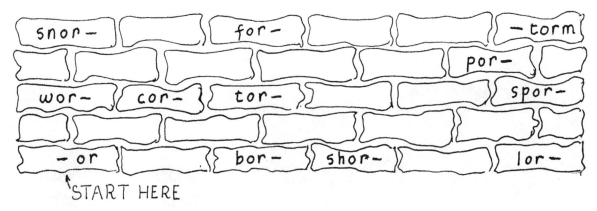

START HERE

Some treasure is hidden behind one of the stones in the wall.
Can you find it by moving from one stone to another?
Fill in the missing letters as you go.

1 Move across two.
2 Move up two.
3 Move across three.
4 Move up two.

Cover the words and write them again. Here is the first letter
of each to help you: f b t s s

3

Write the first letter of each object to spell a word.

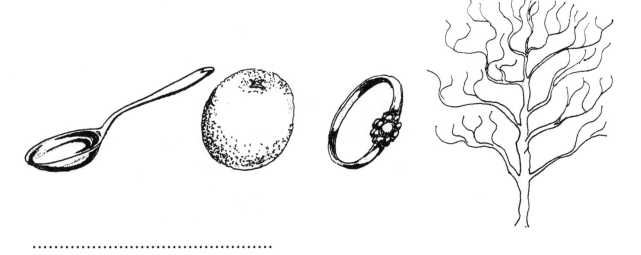

....

Now cover the word and write it again.

8 Fish around for 'sh'

shop	wish
ship	fish
shut	dish
short	push
	crash

Which two letters are in every word? ....
What sound do the letters make?
Put a ring round the word at the top of the page which has
the letters.

1

Can you find four objects with **'sh'** in the picture?
Write the name of each.

Fresh
daily
from our
own ship

Now cover the words and write them again. Here is the first
letter of each to help you: sh sh f d

Key word go

Pirate adventure

left   start here   right

Help! You have been taken by pirates and now you are being held on their ship. Can you escape? Read on. Start at the cross and mark your way out through the ship with a pencil. Fill the gaps with the words in the box

wish shut short push crash

1 You creep to the right along the lower deck until you come to a ladder.

2 You go up the ladder. You find yourself on the gun deck. How you .... you had never been taken by pirates.

3 You go to your left until you come to a ladder. You look behind you and see a .... fat pirate coming for you.

4 You run up the ladder. You slam the door hard to make sure it is .... You hear the pirate fall back with a

    ....

5 Now you are on the top deck. Five pirates come for you, but you .... them off. Then you dive into the sea and swim away.

Did you come out by the ladder on the left?
Cover the five words and write them again. Here is the first letter of each to help you: **w sh sh c p**

9 March along with 'ch'

chips   punch
chop   lunch
chin   bunch
torch   march
pinch   branch

Which two letters are in every word? ....
What sound do the letters make?
Put a ring round the word at the top of the page which has the letters.

1

Can you find four objects with **'ch'** in the picture?
Write the name of each.

Now cover the words and write them again. Here is the first letter of each to help you: b   t   ch   ch

Key word   so

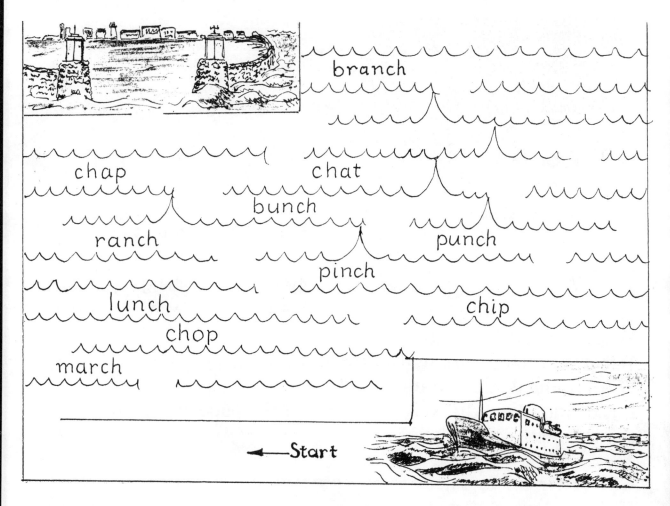

2

Help the captain of the ship find his way through stormy seas and get back to port. Track the route with a pencil. Write down the words with **'ch'** as you meet them on the way.

branch

chap   chat

bunch

ranch   punch

pinch

lunch   chip

chop

march

◄——Start

Now cover the words and write them again. Here is the first letter of each to help you: m   ch   p   p   b

3

What does the hedgehog have for his lunch?
Prickled onions.

Put a ring round the word with **'ch'**
and write it. Then cover it
and write it again.

....

10 Think hard about 'th'

that   thin
than   this
thank   think
then   thing
them   with

Which two letters are in every word? ....
What sound do the letters make?
Put a ring round the word at the top of the page which has the letters.

1

What do you get if you cross a cow with a duck?
Cream quackers.

Put a ring round the word with **'th'** and write it. ....
Now cover it and write it again.

Key word   do

2

Look at the picture. Read the sentence
aloud. Then copy it, saying each word.
Put a line under each word with **'th'**.

I think that this man is thin.

....

Read the sentence until you can remember it.
Then cover it and write it again.

3

Which dog lives in which kennel? Write the name of each dog
and the words on the kennel he lives in. Then cover the words
and write them again.

than
thank

then

them
thing

SPOT   SAM   PIP

Revision

A Five of the bricks in the wall have real words.
Write each word.

sort   nuk   swit   march   pult
wozt   sharp   twok   cwan
think   maf   far   merg

Now cover the words and write them again. Here is the first
letter of each to help you: **s   m   sh   th   f**

B Use the clues and fill
the spaces.

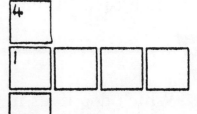

Across
1 Bert is taller ___ Ben.
2 A dog can do it.
3 The string is not long. It is ___ .

Down
2 The baby is one day old. She was ___ yesterday.
4 You may see it in the sky.

Write the words you have written. Then cover them and write
them again. Here is the first letter of each to help you:
th b sh b s

11 Don't duck 'ck'

back	sack	lick	sock	stuck
black	neck	pick	lock	luck

Which two letters are in every word? ....
What is just before the letters?
Put a ring round the word at the top of the page which has the letters.

1

Fill the gaps in this puzzle with the words in the box.

> socks   black   lick   necks   back

Nick has been given a cat and her kitten. They are .... with

white marks on their .... and feet like ties and .... Nick

likes to see the cat .... her kitten all 'over.

Key word   you

Nick has cut two holes in the ....
door so that the cat and her kitten can get in
and out of the house.

Why did his friends laugh at him?

Cover the words you have used and write them again. Here is
the first letter of each to help you: b n s l b

Look at the picture. Read the sentence aloud. Then copy it,
saying each word. Put a line under each word with **'ck'**.

Bad luck! Pick the lock that stuck.

....

Read the sentence until you can remember it. Then cover it and
write it again.

Who gets the sack as soon as he starts work?
A postman.

Put a ring round the word ending in **'ck'** and write it. ....
Now cover it and write it again.

12 Going well with 'll'

sell   will
tell   hill
well   doll
fell   bull
fill   full

Which two letters are in every word? ....
What is just before the letters?
Put a ring round the word at the top of the page which has the letters.

1

Look down and across the lines and find five words ending in 'll'. Colour each one and write it.

```
m e x b f v o f u l l
b l a o x n c e z u s
p k u l s d o l l c s
u f t s t y i p e y k
k l s t i w f d e s t
f s y g f i l l k d q
c k j y k l n z e o n
d y s e l l t n m p i
z x n f o u p u o b v
```

Now cover the words and write them again. Here is the first letter of each to help you: s   f   f   d   w

Key word   my

2

Look at the picture. Read the sentence aloud. Then copy it, saying each word. Put a line under each word with '**ll**'.

Tell Dad the bull fell in the well.

....

Read the sentence until you can remember it. Then cover it and write it again.

3

What is the difference between a hill and a pill?
One goes up and the other goes down.

Put a ring round the two words ending in '**ll**' and write them.

....

Now cover the words and write them again.

13 Have a ball with 'all'

all	hall
ball	small
call	tall
fall	wall

Which three letters are in every word? ....
What sound do the letters make?
Put a ring round the word at the top of the page which has the letters.

1

What did the big tap say to the small tap?
You little squirt.

Put a ring round the word with **'all'** and write it.

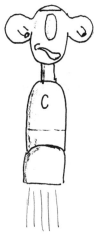
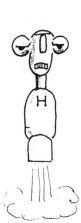

....

Now cover the word and write it again.

Key word we

Write the word for each picture. Then cover the two words and write them again.

....

Write the first letter of each object. Then add **'all'** to make a word. Write each word.

   ....

   ....

   ....

          ....

Now cover the four words and write them again. The first letter of each picture will help you to remember them.

I'll get you back later!

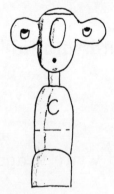

14 Don't miss 'ss'

dress	miss
less	toss
press	boss
mess	cross
chess	fuss

Which two letters are in every word? ....
What is just before the letters?
Put a ring round the word at the top of the page which has the letters.

1

Use the clues and write the word. Then cover it and write it again.

....

Key word   be

2

Look at the picture. Read the sentence aloud. Then copy it, saying each word. Put a line under each word with **'ss'**.

**Miss is cross at
the mess on that dress**

....

....

Read the sentence until you can remember it. Then cover it and write it again.

3

Robbers have hidden a box of jewels under the bush marked **x**. Can you cross the river by the stepping stones and get to it? Fill in the vowel on each word.

Write each word. Then cover the five words and write them again. Here is the first letter of each to help you:

f ch b pr t

15 We're off with 'ff'

cliff	off
sniff	puff
stiff	stuff

Which two letters are in every word? ....
What is just before the letters?
Put a ring round the word at the top of the page which has the letters.

1

Who's that at the door?
A woman with a pram.
Tell her to push off.

Put a ring round the word with **'ff'**
and write it.

....

Now cover the word and write it again.

Key word me

2 Fill in the crossword puzzle.

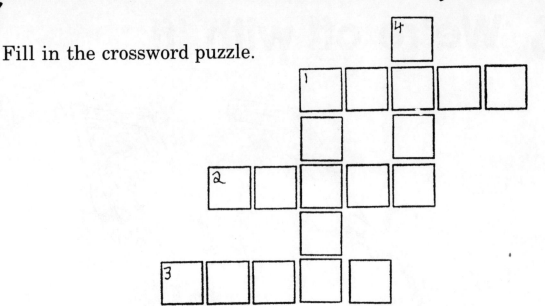

Across
1 If you eat a lot you — yourself.
2 Steep rock by the sea.
3 When you smell something you may — at it.

Down
1 Rhymes with 3 across.
4 A — of smoke.

Cover the words and write them again. Here is the first letter of each to help you: s   c   s   s   p

She took the hint!

Revision

A Look across the lines and find the five words below.
Colour each word and write it.

| stuck   fell   puff   stiff   luck |

v g z v g t k p q m
s t u c k m i g
g p f e l l
y t c x
s e
a f r l
k p u f f c
x q b s t i f f
i r l u c k g a w n

Now cover the words and write them again. Here is the first
letter of each to help you: s f p s l

B Fill the gaps in the story with the words below.

| mess   walls   falls   hall   black |

Mum has been shopping. She has a new .... dress. When
she gets home she is wearing it. She opens the front door and
steps into the .... Dad is painting the .... red. 'Look
out!' he yells. Too late! Mum .... over the tin of paint. She
lands on the floor. Mum looks at her black and red dress and
she screams. Dad moans. 'You've made a .... of my paint,'
he says.

Write the words you have written. Then cover them and write
them again. Here is the first letter of each to help you:
b h w f m

16 A wash line of 'wa' words

want	wasp
wash	swan
wand	swap
was	what (with an 'h')

Which two letters are in every word? ....
What sound do the letters make?
Put a ring round the word at the top of the page which has the letters.

1

Use the clues to find four words with **'wa'**. Write each word.

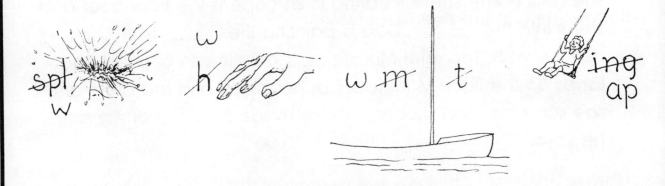

Now cover the words and write them again. Here is the first letter of each to help you: w   w   w   s

Key word your

© Patricia Lewis, Basil Blackwell Ltd 199

2

Look at the picture. Read the sentence aloud. Then copy it, saying each word. Put a line under the words with 'wa'.

What can the swan want with that wasp?

....

Read the sentence until you can remember it. Then cover it and write it again.

3

Why is the letter 't' like an island?
Because it is in the middle of water.

Put a ring round the 'wa' word and write it.

....

How is this word different from the other 'wa' words you have learned?

Now cover the word and write it again.

17 Warm up with 'war'

war   ward
warn   reward
warm   forwards
dwarf   towards
swarm

Which three letters are in every word? ....
What sound do the letters make?
Put a ring round the word at the top of the page which has
the letters.

1

Take these beds *for* the *wards*.   Carry them *to* the *wards*.

Which two words do these pictures help you to spell?
Write them.

....

Cover the two words and write them again.

Key word	they

2

Look at the picture. Read the sentence aloud. Then copy it, saying each word. Put a line under each word with **'war'**.

Swarms go for the dwarf as he gets back from the war.

....

Read the sentence until you can remember it. Then cover it and write it again.

3

The Black Guards of Sug

You are escaping from the Castle of Sug where you have been held for weeks. You have to get past the Black Guards at the gate. You need four passwords. If you can write them all you will be free.

1 Opposite of *cold* ....

2 If you find something
   lost you may get this. r........................... .

3 Hospital room with beds ....

4 Someone may .... you of danger.

Now cover the words and write them again. Here is the first letter of each to help you: w   r   w   w

18 Go to work on 'wor'

word   worth
work   worse
world   worst
worm

Which three letters are in every word? ....
What sound do the letters make?
Put a ring round the word at the top of the page which has
the letters.

1

Look at the picture. Read the sentence aloud. Then copy it,
saying each word. Put a line under each word with **'wor'**.

My word! Dad's work is the worst in the world.

....

Read the sentence until you can remember it. Then cover it
and write it again.

Key word have

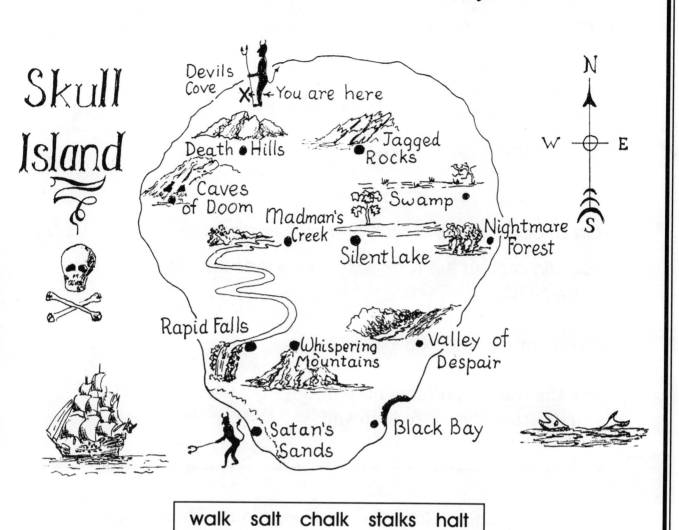

Skull Island

| walk | salt | chalk | stalks | halt |

1 You land at Devil's Cove. You .... south to

   _____ .

2 You go east to _____. Here, you rest for a while.

3 Next, you move south to_____ . Growing beside

   the lake is a huge green plant with thick ....

4 To your amazement, the plant speaks. It tells you to go west.

   You do this and soon you come to_____ .

   You decide to .... here and look for the gold.

   But then you hear a voice calling softly to you from the south,

   so off you go.

5 You find that the call came from _____ .

It tells you to go west to _____ .

6 You soon arrive. You dip a shell into the water and drink some.

It tastes of ....

7 You turn and run south until you reach_____ .

On a rock you see a skull and crossbones drawn in ....

You dig around the rock with your hands until you come to
– the GOLD.

Did you end up in Satan's Sands?

Cover the words you have used and write them again. Here is
the first letter of each to help you: w t f s h

3

Look at the picture. Read the sentence aloud. Then copy it,
saying each word. Put a line under each word with **'al'**.

Dad is bald and talks a lot.

....

Read the sentence until you can remember it. Then cover it
and write it again.

Revision

A Use the clues and fill the spaces.

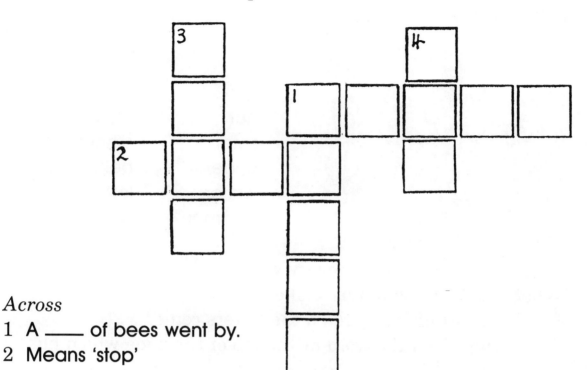

Across

1 A ___ of bees went by.
2 Means 'stop'

Down

1 A flower has a ___ .
3 Use the letters in 'wasp' to make this word meaning 'change'.
4 Last week Tom ___ not very well.

Write the words you have used. Then cover them and write them again. Here is the first letter of each to help you:

s   h   s   s   w

B Look at this word: war

See if you can make two more words by adding the letters:

d f   t o d s

Write the words you have made. Then cover them and write them again. Here is the first letter of each to help you:

d   t

20 You'll feel better with 'er'

her	silver
sister	dinner
under	better
winter	letter
summer	butter

Which two letters are in every word? ....
What sound do the letters make?
In which part of the word do the letters come?
Put a ring round the word at the top of the page which has the letters.

Fill in the crossword puzzle.

Across
1 You may have a brother or a ____ .
2 You eat bread and ____ .
3 A ring may be made of gold or ____ .

Down
4 If you practise, your spelling will get ____ .
5 Winter is cold but ____ is warm.

Key word live

Cover the words and write them again. Here is the first letter of each to help you: s b s b s

2

Look at the picture. Fill the gaps with words from the list.

The time of the year is ....

The Smith family are eating their ....

The dog is .... the table.

Dad is reading a ....

Now cover the words and write them again. Here is the first letter of each to help you: w u d l

3

Why did the girl keep a loaf in her comic?

She liked crummy jokes.

Put a ring round the word with **'er'** and write it.

....

Cover the word and write it again.

21 Look happy with 'y' endings

funny	silly
happy	empty
plenty	windy
twenty	Mummy
sorry	Daddy

Which letter is in every word? ....

What sound does the letter make?

In which part of the word does the letter come? ....

Put a ring round the word at the top of the page which has the letter.

To help you — The ⓟa i l is e mⓟt y.

1

Use the clue and spell a word ending in 'y'.

h s y

....

Cover the word and write it again.

Key word no

2

Find five words ending in 'y'. Look across and down the lines. Colour each word and then write it.

```
b h j p i o m l i t h
a e m p t y r g u g j
s g t o p l e n t y n
o k h l e D u s c b e
r h q t j a m j t x k
r g t u o d h r f a p
y t r c x d z e y r t
g M u m m y b t m z y
n m j i o p v t d r t
d f t r h r e y t f b
```

Now cover the words and write them again. Here is the first letter of each to help you: e p s M D

3

Write the word ending in 'y' for each picture.

Now cover the four words and write them again. Here is the first letter of each to help you: h w f t

22 Go fast with these words

last	grass	rather
fast	after	bath
ask	nasty	father

Which letter is in every word? ....
What sound do the letters make?
Put a ring round the word at the top of the page which has the letter.

1

Read the sentence aloud. Then copy it, saying each word.
Put a line under each word with '**a**' with the sound /**ar**/.

After work Father would rather have a bath than cut the grass.

Read the sentence until
you can remember it.
Then cover it and
write it again.

Key words could would should

2

Adventure in Devil's Caves

You have spent the day in Devil's Caves. Now it is time to get out and go home. But – oh help! You can't find the way.

Read on. Track your way between the dots on the map with a pencil.

Fill the gaps marked __ with the names of the dangers you come to. Fill the gaps marked ..... with the words in the box.

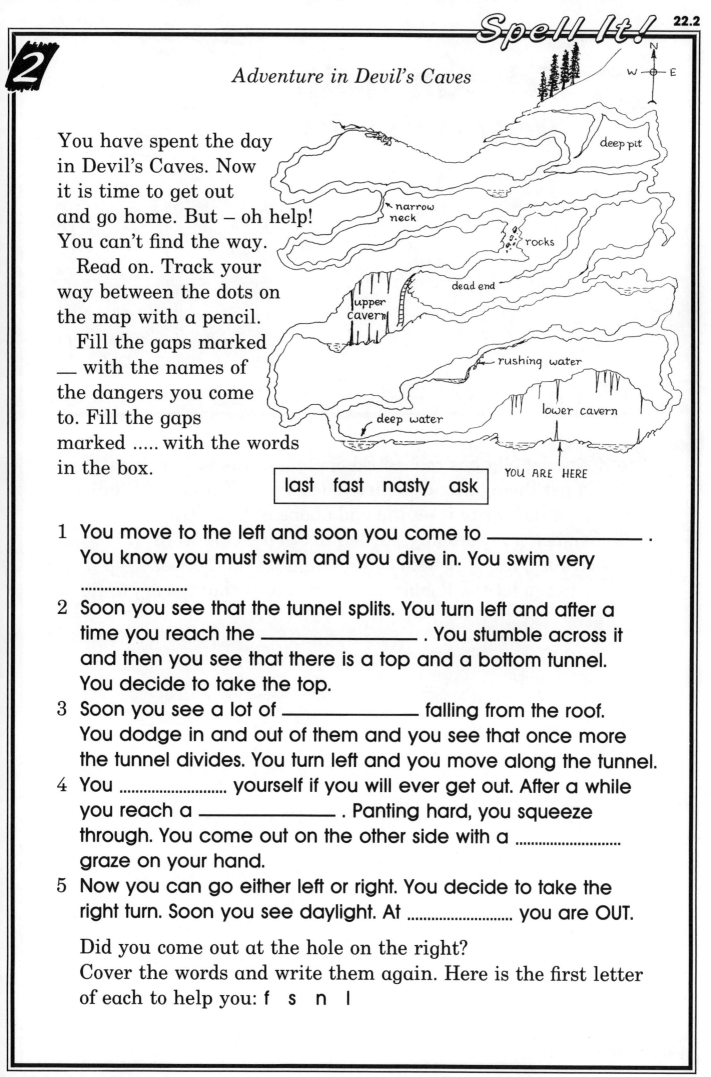

deep pit

narrow neck

rocks

dead end

upper cavern

rushing water

lower cavern

deep water

YOU ARE HERE

| last | fast | nasty | ask |

1 You move to the left and soon you come to _____ .
You know you must swim and you dive in. You swim very

....

2 Soon you see that the tunnel splits. You turn left and after a time you reach the _____ . You stumble across it and then you see that there is a top and a bottom tunnel. You decide to take the top.

3 Soon you see a lot of _____ falling from the roof. You dodge in and out of them and you see that once more the tunnel divides. You turn left and you move along the tunnel.

4 You .... yourself if you will ever get out. After a while you reach a _____ . Panting hard, you squeeze through. You come out on the other side with a ....
graze on your hand.

5 Now you can go either left or right. You decide to take the right turn. Soon you see daylight. At .... you are OUT.

Did you come out at the hole on the right?
Cover the words and write them again. Here is the first letter of each to help you: f s n l

23 Ed can help you write in the past

1

The Robber of Nig has robbed Ed of eight of his 'ed' endings.
Help Ed get them back. Complete each word. If it ends in **'ed'**
cross it out and write it on the end of one of Ed's strings.

Remember, you can only put **'ed'** on to a whole word. If it is not
a whole word, finish it with 'd' or 't' and let the Robber keep it.
Be sure not to let the Robber keep any words that belong to Ed.

_____ slep
_____ fis-
_____ bes-
_____ lis-
_____ fas-
_____ las-

fish-

crash-
bark-
sort-
pack-
wish-
march-
punch-
len-

Key word	said

3

Who stole the money?

My name is Jo Betts. I am the manager of a bank.
These people are my staff.

Ned Smith   John Brown   Ann Pitt   Sally Farmer   Jane Wells

The bank was shut. It was nearly time to go home. The staff
started to clear up. I opened the safe. I gasped – for I could
see at once that some money was missing. I called the staff
together. I told them that someone had taken money from the
safe. 'Which one of you took it?' I asked.

Each person said that they had not been to the safe that day.

'One of you is lying,' I said. 'One of you did enter the safe
today. I know because I found something there belonging to
one of you.'

Look at the five people and you will see that someone has
something missing. Who was lying and what did Jo Betts find?

Find the four words ending in 'ed' and write them.

Now write each sentence in the present by taking the **'ed'**
ending off the word, like this –

The staff started to clear up   The staff start to clear up

Revision

A Fill the gaps in the story with the words below.

silver fast summer empty last

Bill Bloggs was a policeman, but not a very clever one. His boss told him that the big house near by had been .... for sometime. All through the .... someone had been pinching apples from the garden. Bill said he would move .... That night when it was dark he went to the house and waited. At .... he saw a man creeping along with a sack on his back. Bill jumped out on him and told him to open the sack. It was full of .... 'Lucky for you it isn't apples,' said Bill. 'Off you go.'

Cover the words you have used and write them again. Here is the first letter of each to help you: e   s   f   l   s

---

B Look across the lines and find the five words below. Colour each word and write it.

her silly after winter funny

```
            m
          h e r
        s i l l y
      j g t y p l h
      g b k a f t e r b
      g w i n t e r h v t q
      c b f u n n y d z k v w u
```

Cover the words and write them again. Here is the first letter of each to help you: h   s   a   w   f

Spell It!

© Patricia Lewis, Basil Blackwell Ltd 1990

24 It's a game with 'a' – consonant – 'e'

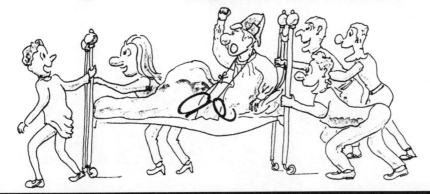

1

Add 'e' to the words below and write the new word. Read both words aloud. The first one has been done for you.

at + e .... ate ....   mad + e ....

hat + e ....   tap + e ....

pal + e ....   pan + e ....

mat + e ....   cap + e ....

Now read these: plate   game
                       gave   name
                       grape   came
                       gate   same

2

Write the first letter of each object and spell a word with **'a'** – **conson**ant – 'e'. Then cover the word and write it again.

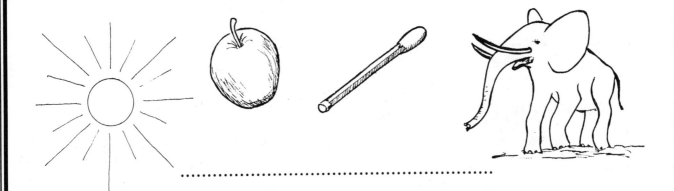

....

Key word   over

3

There are five words with **'a' – consonant – 'e'** in this picture. Write the word for each.

Now cover the five words and write them again. Here is the first letter of each to help you: **p p g t g**

4

Fill the gaps in this sentence with the words in the box.

| game   came   made |

Yesterday my friend .... and we .... a ....

Cover the words and write them again. Here is the first letter of each to help you: **c   m   g**

25 Don't let 'a' 'r' 'e' scare you

bare   stare
care   scare
share   dare
fare (bus, etc)   hare (animal)
spare   square

Which three letters are in every word? ....
What sound do the letters make?
Put a ring round the word at the top of the page which has
the letters.

1

How many squares can you find
in this drawing?

There are ....

Cover the **'are'** word you have
used and write it again.

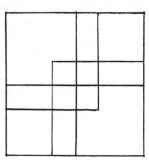

2

Add **'are'** to the letter and write the word. The first one has
been done for you.

1st letter   1st letter

c .... + ... are = care   ....

Key word when

1st and 2nd letter

1st and 2nd letter

....

Now write these words without looking at them. Here is the first letter of each to help you: c   s   h   s

3

Which pilot flies which plane? Write the name of each pilot and the words on the banner of the plane he flies.

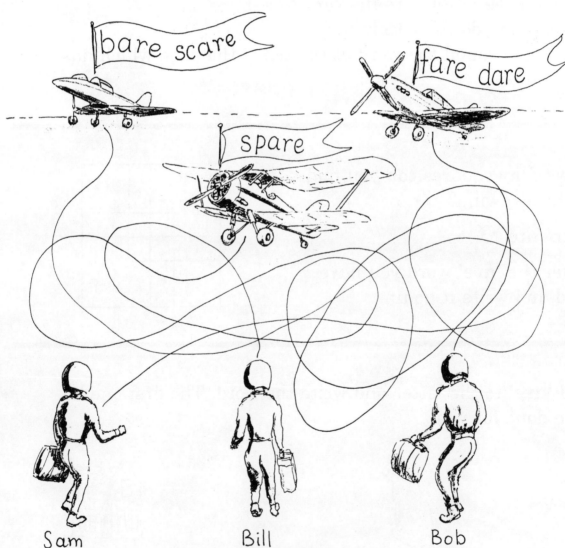

bare scare

fare dare

spare

Sam   Bill   Bob

Now cover the words and write them again. Here is the first letter of each: b   f   s   d   s

26 Smile with 'i' – consonant – 'e'

1

Add **'e'** to the words below and write the new word. Read both words aloud.

rip + e .... ripe ....   hid + e ....

pip + e ....   Tim + e ....

fin + e ....   Sid + e ....

rid + e ....   quit + e ....

bit + e ....

Now read these words: white   fire   inside

2

There was a young lady from Riga
Who rode with a smile on a tiger.
They returned from the ride
With the lady inside
And a smile on the face of the tiger.

Key words   ever   never

Put a ring round the three words with **'i' – consonant – 'e'** and write them. Then cover them and write them again. Here is the first letter of each to help you: s r i

3

Look at the picture. Read the sentence aloud. Then copy it, saying each word. Underline the words with **'i' – consonant – 'e'**.

Dad hides with his pipe and his wine and has a fine time.

....

....

Read the sentence until you can remember it.
Then cover it and write it again.

4

Fill the gaps with the words in the box.

| white   fire   quite   side |

How to make transfer mixture

This is .... an easy way to make a transfer of a picture.

You will need:

> white spirit
>
> a screwtop jar
>
> soap
>
> a painting brush
>
> a sheet of white paper
>
> a board
>
> drawing pins
>
> a magazine picture

1 Put ten large spoonfuls of water into the jar. Add one spoonful of white spirit and a piece of soap the size of a pea. Keep the white spirit away from ....

2 Shake the jar well, then leave for a day or so for the soap to melt.

3 Put the magazine picture on the board. Dab the transfer mixture over the picture with the brush.

4 Put the sheet of .... paper over the picture and pin it to the board.

5 With the back of the spoon rub hard where the paper covers the picture. This will transfer the ink in the picture to the under .... of the white paper.

6 Lift the paper to see how the transfer is coming on. Add more mixture, if need be, until the transfer is complete.

Cover the words you have used and write them again.
Here is the first letter of each to help you: f   q   w   s

27 You can cope with 'o' – consonant – 'e'

1

Add **'e'** to each word and write the new word. Read both words aloud.

hop + e .... hope ....   pop + e ....

rod + e ....   slop + e ....

cod + e ....   cop + e ....

not + e ....   rob + e ....

cloth + es ....

Read aloud: those   hole   home   nose

bone   rose   rope

2

Fill the gaps below with the words in the box.

home   hope   note   clothes   those

Peter and Ben were twins. They loved puzzles and they were always trying to catch each other out. 'I .... you haven't heard this one,' said Peter one day. 'The Smiths had a dog who was a bit of a pest. He jumped up at people and spoilt their .... and things like that. One day, Mrs Smith got .... from work and found that the dog had chewed up a .... she had written for the milkman. She was so fed up that she tied the dog up in the garden. 'And don't you dare dig up .... seeds I planted,' she yelled at him.

Soon, the dog saw a bone, but it was three metres away and the rope he was tied to was only one metre long. How could the dog reach the bone?'

Key word   next

Ben thought hard. 'I give up,' he said at last.
Peter laughed. 'The rope isn't tied to anything,' he said.

Cover the words you have used and write them again. Here is
the first letter of each to help you: h c h n th

3

Can you find three objects with **'o' – consonant – 'e'** in the
picture?
Write the words. Then cover the words
and write them again.

....

4

What do you get if you pour
boiling water down a rabbit hole?
Hot cross bunnies.

Put a ring round the word with
'o' – consonant – 'e' and write it.

....

Cover the word and write it again.

28 Cure your problems with 'u' - consonant - 'e'

1

Add **'e'** to the words below and write the new word. Read both words aloud.

cub + e .... cube ....   cut + e ....

tub + e ....   us + e ....

Read aloud: rude   refuse

                           June   cure

                           tune   sure

2

What should you do if a baby swallows your biro?
Use a pencil instead.

Put a ring round the word with
'u' – consonant – 'e' and write it.

....

Then cover the word and write it again.

Key word	very

3

Write the word for each picture. Then cover the three words and write them again.

   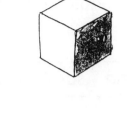

....

4

Mountain Adventure

You are going on holiday by plane to France. As you are flying over the Alps the plane's engine fails. The plane dives downwards and crashes into the mountain.

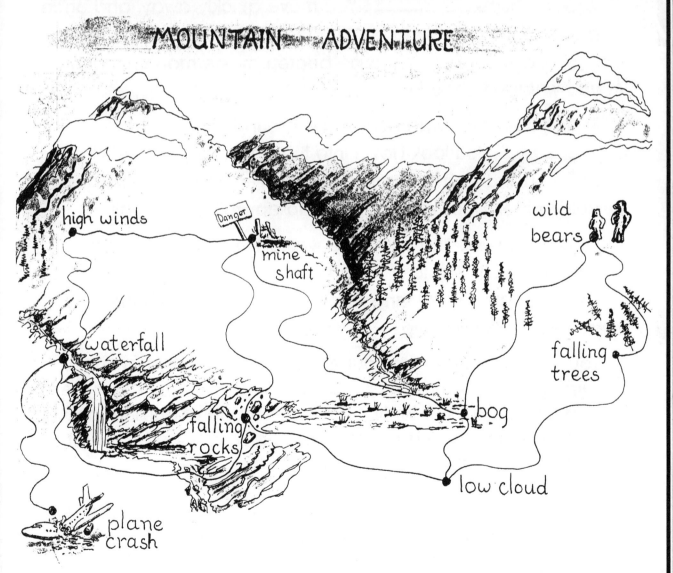

You are the only one to live. You must try to find your way out of the mountain. Track your way on the map with a pencil. Fill the gaps marked ___ in the passage with the names of the dangers you meet. Fill the gaps marked .... with the words in the box.

cures June sure tune refuse

1 You decide to move up the mountain. It is hard work and you grow very thirsty. Soon you come to a huge _____. You drink some of the ice-cold water and it .... your thirst.

2 You see that you cannot go up any further, so you climb around the waterfall. Then you start moving down the mountain. Suddenly you hear a crashing sound behind you. You see huge _____ . You move quickly away, and once more you start to climb up. You feel very hot, for it is a warm .... day. You .... to be beaten by the mountain and you whistle a cheerful ....

3 Soon you see a large hole in the ground. It is an old _____ . You look down into the darkness. You feel dizzy and you find yourself starting to fall over the edge. You quickly pull yourself back. You turn and go down the mountain.

4 Before long you find you have walked into some _____ . You are beginning to sink. You grab the branch of a tree and soon you are on dry land again. To get away from the bog you turn and climb up.

5 You climb for nearly an hour. Suddenly you hear growling. Turning, you see three _____ . You feel .... this is the end for you. But suddenly there is the sound of gunshot and the bears run off. Coming towards you is a rescue party. You are safe!

Cover the words you have used and write them again. Here is the first letter of each to help you: c j r t s